Photocopiable activities for

Physical Development

Jenni Tavener

Author
Jenni Tavener

Editor
Jane Bishop

Assistant editor
Susan Howard

Series designer
Joy White

Designer
Sarah Rock

Illustrations
Lynne Farmer

Cover photo
Martyn Chillmaid

For Leah

Published by Scholastic Ltd, Villiers House, Clarendon Avenue,
Leamington Spa, Warwickshire CV32 5PR

© 1999 Scholastic Ltd   Text © 1999 Jenni Tavener
1 2 3 4 5 6 7 8 9 0   9 0 1 2 3 4 5 6 7 8

British Library Cataloguing-in-Publication Data
A catalogue record for this book is available from the British Library.

ISBN 0-590-53882-9

Contents

Introduction

Physical Development is an ideal curriculum area to provide exciting and enticing activities to encourage children to learn. In addition, the activities in this book can be used to stimulate the children's interest in other areas of the curriculum. While developing co-ordination skills, for example, the children could also be gaining skills in creativity, language and mathematics with activities which involve sewing, handling puppets, and following codes.

Most children love to be active or busy; Physical Development can be used to channel this 'activity' into positive and purposeful learning situations.

Desirable Outcomes for Physical Development

The activities in this book focus on both gross and fine motor skills in accordance with the *Desirable Outcomes for Children's Learning* as identified by the School Curriculum and Assessment Authority (SCAA).

The book covers all the appropriate areas of learning within four chapters:

Manipulative skills – activities to help children develop skills in hand control and in manipulating small and large objects. There are also opportunities to practise handwriting patterns and to use scissors to cut a variety of materials with increasing accuracy.

Co-ordination skills – activities to develop hand and eye co-ordination and to encourage the development of fine and gross motor skills with tasks such as making toys and playing physical games. There are also a range of activities to help develop pre-writing skills and pencil control.

Balance and awareness of space – ideas to develop the children's spatial awareness and large body movements by offering a variety of action games and ideas for dance and mime. There are also opportunities for children to explore different body shapes and ways of balancing their body while involved in exciting activities which can be played indoors or outdoors.

Using malleable materials – a range of purposeful, tactile experiences to help develop the children's manual dexterity and fine motor skills. They will be involved in making mud pies, constructing three-dimensional pictures and creating soft toys, among many other exciting activities which will help them to explore different types of malleable materials.

Many other opportunities to encourage gross motor skills are also included in this book with photocopiable activities to inspire the use of small apparatus (balls, beanbags) and the use of low level apparatus (obstacles to go through, around, under and along).

How to use the book

The chapter titles in this book link with those in its sister book *Learning in the Early Years – Physical Development*; the 'Using large equipment' chapter is not included as it is inappropriate for the photocopiable format of this book as

photocopiable-based activities largely rely on their visual attraction, which could be an unwelcome distraction if used in conjunction with large apparatus.

The Learning in the Early Years series comprises two sets of books, *Learning in the Early Years* (covering activities, some photocopiables, child development, planning the curriculum, record keeping) and *Learning in the Early Years Photocopiable Activities*. Each area of learning has two books devoted to it, the original book and its photocopiable partner. In addition there is a series handbook *Ready for Inspection*. These books are designed to complement each other but they can all equally well stand alone as independent resources.

The activity chapters in this book follow the same format, providing two sections:

Activity notes – the main aims of the chapter are highlighted. There are then specific notes for each photocopiable sheet under the headings 'Learning Objective' and 'What to do', which explain exactly how to use each sheet, including how many children can be involved, and the resources needed.

Photocopiable activities – each photocopiable sheet provides the basis of a 'free-standing' activity. Many of the sheets can be adapted by enlarging or reducing them in size on the photocopier, and by laminating them they can be used in the future. The activities provide a wide range of different approaches for encouraging 'Physical Development', for example, some photocopiable sheets are designed to be turned into gameboards ('The caterpillar game' page 63), action game cards ('Where's that dragon?' pages 48 and 49) or booklets ('I can... booklet' page 43).

Some of the photocopiable sheets can be used for Record Keeping and Assessment, for example 'The magic carpet' (page 14) can be used to record skills in colour identification, 'The apple tree game' (page 17) can be used to assess counting skills up to six and 'A sailor went to sea' (page 31) can be used to assess and record pencil control.

Resources

All the activities make use of resources which are easily accessible in any early years environment, for example sand, coloured pens, paint, scissors, glue, fabric, clay, dough, dice, construction kits, play utensils and display boards. By using a wide variety of resources you will help the children to gain firsthand experience of handling objects which will aid their overall development.

Links with home

Many of the photocopiable sheets can be used as Homelinks activities to help encourage a positive liaison between home and school/nursery. Some sheets could go home with the children to be completed with their parents, others, such as the board games and booklet could be completed at school/nursery and then taken home to share with parents as follow-up activities.

chapter one

Manipulative skills

The range of activities in this chapter aim to help children develop their dexterity in manipulative skills. The variety of approaches suggested will help to maintain the children's interest and enthusiasm while they practise new skills.

Spiral mobiles
Learning objective
To develop hand control.
What to do
Provide each child with an A4 or A3 photocopy of the sheet, and a selection of paint brushes in different sizes. Invite the children to select an appropriate sized brush to paint each spiral in their choice of colours. When the paint is dry, help the children to cut around the black lines to create one large and one small spiral. Tape some thread to the centre of each spiral, and hang them from a large hoop. Place the spirals in a draft to create an interesting mobile.

The colourful caterpillar
Learning objective
To select and handle small objects with increasing control. To develop skills in manipulating a 'rod-puppet'.
What to do
Provide the children with shallow trays of paint and a selection of four small objects for printing (such as Unifix cubes or cotton reels). Invite them to print a different pattern in each segment of the caterpillar. When dry, help them to cut out the caterpillar and to tape a lolly-stick (or ruler) at each end to create a 'wriggly rod-puppet'.

Flower circles
Learning objective
To develop pencil holding skills; to practise a circular handwriting pattern.
What to do
Show the children how to hold their pencils correctly before you begin.

Encourage them to each place a pencil on the dot of each circle and to follow the circular shape in an anticlockwise direction; this is the direction they will follow when they write the letters o, a, c, d, g and q. When complete, invite the children to colour in their circles to create a 'flower' and display them together.

Ladybird, ladybird
Learning objective
To develop colouring, cutting and gluing skills; to use sticky tape with accuracy.
What to do
Provide each child with an A4 copy of the sheet and encourage them to colour the ladybird using red crayons and to cut out the four black spots to stick onto the red wings. Invite the children to use sticky tape to secure six black pipe-cleaners to the ladybird to create legs.

Funny hats
Learning objective
To develop scissor skills; to experience manipulating fabric.
What to do
Hand out a copy of the sheet to individual children and invite them to cut shapes from fabric to create an original hat for each character. Let the children glue their hats in place and then decorate them using ribbons, beads, lace, buttons and feathers.

The magic carpet
Learning objective
To develop hand control.
What to do
Give each child a copy of the sheet and invite them to choose four colours to complete their colour code. Reinforce how to hold pens/pencils correctly to produce controlled colouring.

PAGE 15

Fishing

Learning objective

To develop threading skills; to encourage planning while handling threads.

What to do

Help the children to prepare for the activity by cutting out the fishing picture and gluing it to card. Use a hole punch to create six randomly placed holes in the picture. Secure approximately 30cm of thread to the picture of the net.

Invite the children to each weave the thread through the six holes with the aim of 'catching' as many fish as possible in the tangled 'net'. Help them to unravel the thread for further turns.

PAGE 16

Five little ducks

Learning objective

To develop cutting and sticking skills; to practise controlling the movements of individual fingers.

What to do

Invite each child to colour in and cut out the five duck pictures. Help them to roll and glue each picture to form five finger-puppet tubes. Encourage the children to manipulate the puppets on their fingers while singing the rhyme 'Five Little Ducks'. Use the puppets in plays and stories. Let the children take their puppets home to practise the rhyme with parents.

PAGE 17

The apple tree game

Learning objective

To position counters and to use a dice.

What to do

This is an A4 game for two players. Photocopy one game sheet. Colour and cut out the game tree (leave the apples white), mount onto card and cover in clear adhesive film to protect it.

Provide one player with six red counters and the other player with six green counters (to represent red and green apples). The first player throws a dice (showing dots, figures or words 1–6). If for example, 3 is shown, that player should place their counter on the apple with three dots; if 3 is already covered the dice is passed to the next player. Play continues until all six apples are covered. The winner is the player with the most apples in their colour.

PAGE 18

Jazzy mobile

Learning objective

To design using pastels or crayons; to manipulate a 2D sheet of paper into a 3D structure.

What to do

Use as an A4 activity for individual children or enlarge for paired work.

Invite the children to fill in the colour code, and to follow their code to transform the black and white pattern into a multicoloured design. Help them to cut around the square containing their design. Show the children how to bend their 2D designs around so that the two corners marked with an X can be glued (or stapled) together to create a 3D structure. Tape a thread to the top and hang to create an unusual mobile.

PAGE 19

Planting and growing

Learning objective

To develop manipulative skills through planting seeds or beans; to reinforce cutting, sticking and folding skills.

What to do

This is an activity for individuals, pairs or small groups. Provide the children with a pot, fertilizer, seeds or beans and show them how to carefully plant their seeds or beans. Place the pots in a sunny position and encourage the children to water them regularly.

As a follow-up activity, provide each child with a copy of the 'planting and growing' sheet and invite them to cut out the pictures and to stick them in the correct order along a strip of paper or card. Help them fold it to create a zigzag book. Use the book to initiate discussion about what plants need, and how to care for them.

PAGE 20

Teddy bear puzzle

Learning objective

To develop hand control.

What to do

This is an A4 activity for individuals or pairs of children. Help each child, or pair of children, to cut along the dotted lines to create four sections. Invite them to manoeuvre the pieces around until they find a picture of a teddy bear waving both hands.

Use the pieces as a jigsaw puzzle or glue them onto card to create a picture.

Spiral mobiles

Paint these spirals.

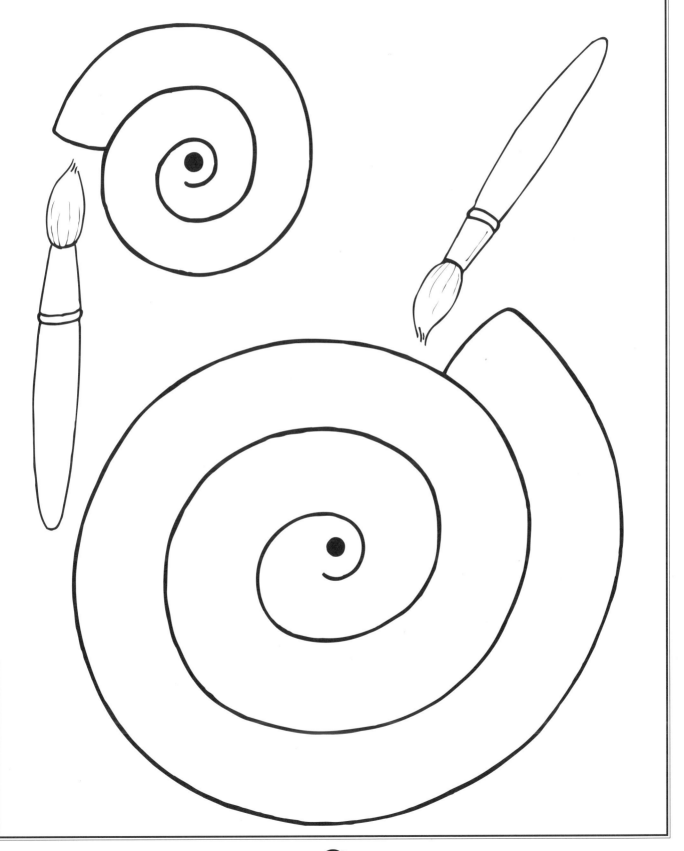

The colourful caterpillar

Print some patterns on the caterpillar.

Flower circles

Place your pencil on each dot. Draw a circle by following the arrow.

Colour in your flower picture.

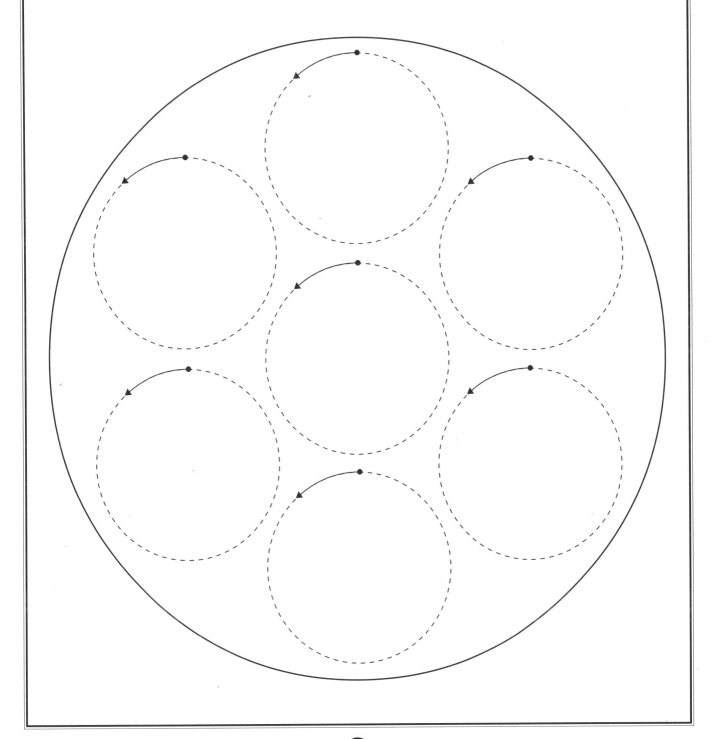

Ladybird, ladybird

Colour in and cut out the ladybird.

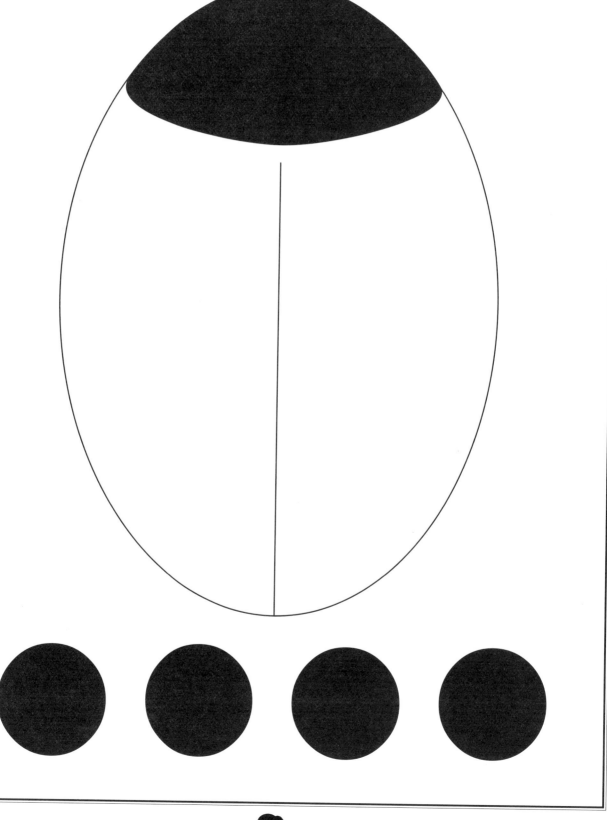

Funny hats

Make funny hats for these faces.

The magic carpet

Choose four colours to fill in a code. Follow your code to decorate the carpet.

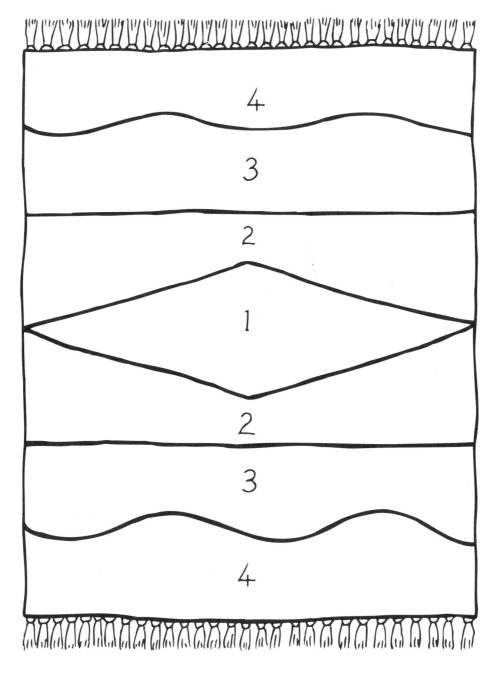

colour code

1= ◯   2= ◯   3= ◯   4= ◯

Fishing

Punch some holes in the picture. Weave thread through the holes to catch the fish.

Five little ducks

Colour in and cut out these ducks and make them into finger puppets.

The apple tree game

Throw a dice. Cover the apples with counters.

Jazzy mobile

Make up your own colour code:

Planting and growing

Colour in and cut out the pictures, and put them in order.

Teddy bear puzzle

Cut out the four sections. Join them together to make a Teddy bear picture.

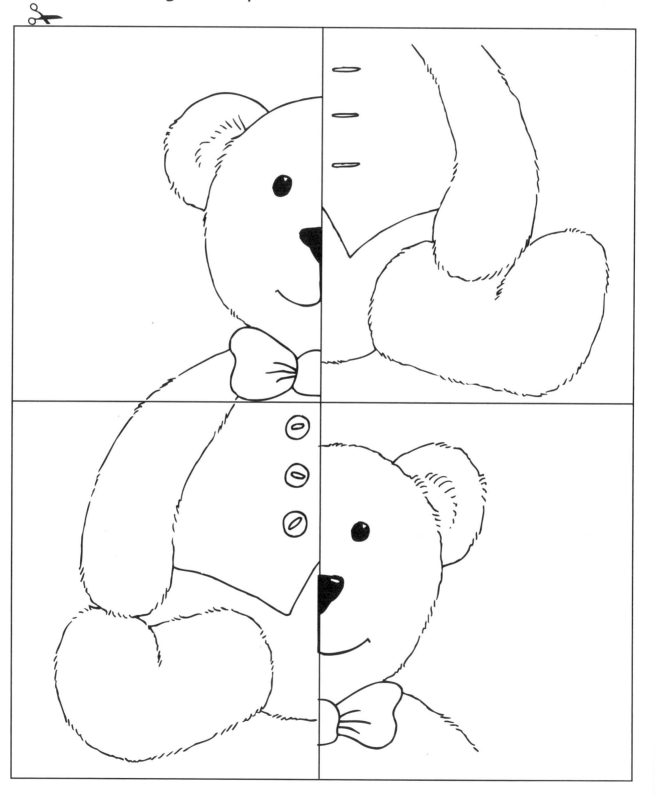

chapter two

Co-ordination skills

Co-ordination skills are very important for young children to acquire, as they affect so many aspects of their overall development. Activities which use fine motor skills such as writing, drawing and small construction activities all require hand and eye co-ordination, as do activities which use gross motor skills such as catching and throwing.

PAGE 24

There was a crooked man
Learning objective
To develop co-ordination when using both hands together.
What to do
Provide one sheet for each child and invite them to colour in and cut out the four pictures.

Help them to attach a length of wool to the top of each character picture and to glue the pictures of the 'crooked mile' onto a box or folded card. Encourage the children to hold the puppets, one in each hand, and using the 'crooked mile' as a backdrop, re-enact the nursery rhyme, or make up their own plays and stories.

PAGE 25

Toy town map
Learning objective
To develop hand and eye co-ordination.
What to do
Enlarge the sheet to A3 to provide an activity for individuals or pairs of children. Encourage them to use construction bricks to build a school, a garage, some shops, houses and flats on the map. Let the children manoeuvre small toy cars or play figures around the route.

For long term use, colour the map, mount it onto card and cover it in clear adhesive film.

PAGE 26

A flying saucer
Learning objective
To develop fine motor skills while constructing and using a 'spinner'.
What to do
Sing the rhyme:
Five little men in their flying saucers
Flew round the world one day

They looked left and right
And didn't like the sight
So one man flew away...
Four little men...

Copy the sheet for each child and help them to cut along the dotted lines. Position the 'wheel' behind the 'window' and secure them together using a paper fastener. Say the rhyme with the children and as you go through it encourage them to co-ordinate turning their wheel in the direction of the arrows so that the correct number of 'spacemen' can be seen in the 'window'.

Picture cards
PAGE 27
Learning objective
To develop practical co-ordination skills while making and using a set of 'playing cards'.
What to do
This is an activity for pairs or small groups. Make two photocopies of the sheet, both in A4, or both A3.

Invite the children to help colour in and cut out the pictures. Mount them onto twelve rectangles of card and cover them in clear adhesive film.

Use the cards to introduce games such as 'Snap' or 'Pairs', or 'Happy families' to the children.

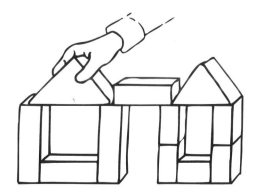

PAGE 28

Sewing a calendar

Learning objective
To develop manual dexterity while using a needle and thread.

What to do
Copy the sheet onto thin card for each child. Prepare the card for sewing by piercing six holes through the dots in each tree. Provide each child with a blunt needle and a selection of threads, buttons and beads in shades of yellow, red, orange and brown.

Invite the children to use the yellow threads, buttons and beads to sew a random pattern through the holes in the tree marked 'spring yellow'. Tape any loose ends of thread on the reverse side. Encourage the children to create one more random design in the other tree.

With younger children, prepare larger holes and provide thick threads without a needle. Hang a calendar at the bottom to make into a seasonal gift.

PAGE 29

Toy box dot-to-dot

Learning objective
To develop hand and eye co-ordination while using a pencil; to encourage cutting and gluing skills.

What to do
Use this as an A4 activity for individuals or an A3 activity for paired work.

Invite the children to use a pencil to join the dots 1–6 to create a 'toy box' outline which can then be coloured in. Encourage them to cut out pictures of toys from old magazines or catalogues to stick in their toy box.

When they are complete, cut out and mount each toy box onto a display board. Use as an interactive display by asking questions such as 'Which toy box has more than five toys inside?', 'Find the toy box with a train set' or 'Describe the toys in the blue toy box'.

PAGE 30

The buns and cakes game

Learning objective
To develop pencil control.

What to do
This is an A4 activity for 2–4 players. Photocopy one sheet for each child. Use a wooden brick to make a dice showing three noughts on three sides and three crosses on the remaining three sides.

How to play: Each player has a sheet. In turn the players throw the dice. If it shows a cross, that player should mark a cross on one of their empty 'hot cross buns'. If it shows a nought, they should draw a round cherry on one of the empty cakes. The dice is then passed to the next player. The winner is the first player to decorate all their buns and cakes with circles and crosses. Afterwards, invite the children to colour in their game sheets and to count the number of cakes and buns.

PAGE 31

A sailor went to sea

Learning objective
To develop pre-writing and co-ordination skills.

What to do
Provide each child with a copy of the sheet and a sharp pencil. Encourage them to follow the 'waves' carefully, in the direction of the arrows. Invite them to colour in the boats and to talk about what is happening in each scene.

PAGE 32

Incy Wincy Spider

Learning objective
To make and use a simple 'toy' with moving parts; to develop co-ordinated hand movements.

What to do
Use as an A4 or A3 activity for individual children. Provide each child with a copy of the sheet to colour in and to cut out. Help them to stick the drainpipe picture onto a large piece of a cereal box or a sheet of folded card. An adult should punch a hole in the top of the drainpipe.

Help the children to stick Incy Wincy Spider onto a circle of card and to attach it to a length of wool or string. They can then thread the wool through the hole in the 'drainpipe' and tie a large knot in the other end of the wool or string. The children should pull the knot to make Incy Wincy climb up the drainpipe. When they let go Incy will fall down again.

PAGE 33

Hands and feet

Learning objective
To develop co-ordination of hands and feet and gross motor skills.

What to do
Make one enlarged photocopy, to

provide an A3 activity for small or large groups of children. Cut out the picture and the spinner, secure onto card and attach the spinner using a paper fastener.

Set up a circular obstacle course in a large room or outside. Include objects to go over, under, around and through. Ensure large spaces are left in between each obstacle.

Position the picture where it can be seen easily. Invite the children to move around the obstacle course and at regular intervals, spin the spinner to show a new way for everyone to move between each obstacle.

Humpty's fall

PAGE 34

Learning objective
To practise target hitting and to develop gross motor skills.

What to do
Enlarge 'Humpty Dumpty' to A3 size and invite the children to help colour

him using paints or crayons. Cut him out, and mount onto an oval of thick card. Cover in clear adhesive film.

Secure the back of Humpty to the rim of a sturdy box using a strip of strong wide tape across the centre of his body (see below left).

Working with small or large groups of children, let them take it in turns to throw sponge balls or beanbags at 'Humpty' in an attempt to knock him backwards. For team games, make a 'Humpty' for each team of children.

Ball rolling

PAGE 35

Learning objective
To encourage ball rolling skills. To develop gross motor skills.

What to do
This is an activity for small or large groups of children. If possible make a small, medium and large photocopy of the dog. Invite the children to help colour the three pictures in using paints or crayons.

Secure the pictures onto three different sized boxes. Stand the boxes on the floor, and invite the children to gently roll some balls towards each dog picture. The aim is to make the balls reach the dog without knocking him over. Challenge the children to use a variety of balls, large and small, hard and soft.

A patterned fish

PAGE 36

Learning objective
To develop hand and eye co-ordination while using pens or pencils; to develop pre-writing skills.

What to do
Provide each child with a copy of the sheet and a selection of brightly coloured pens, crayons or pencils.

Encourage them to follow the patterns on the fish carefully in the direction of the arrows, and then to continue the same pattern to the end of the space. Encourage them to complete the 'bubbles' in one circular movement.

Alternatively, enlarge the fish picture to A3 size, and provide the children with coloured paints and a good quality paint brush. Encourage them to complete the patterns using paint.

There was a crooked man

Colour and cut out the pictures.

Toy town map

Make a town on your map. Can you drive some cars on the road?

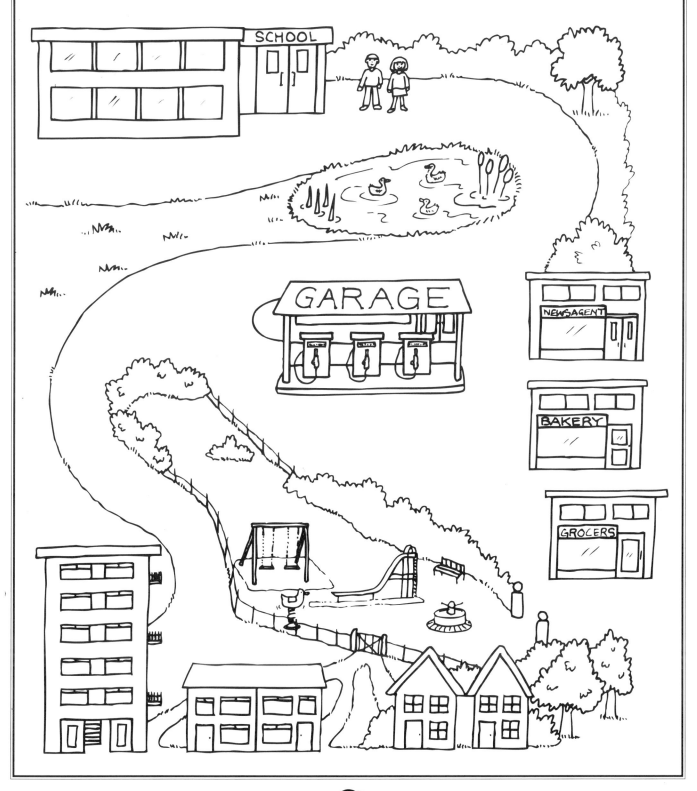

A flying saucer

Make this spinner with a helper.

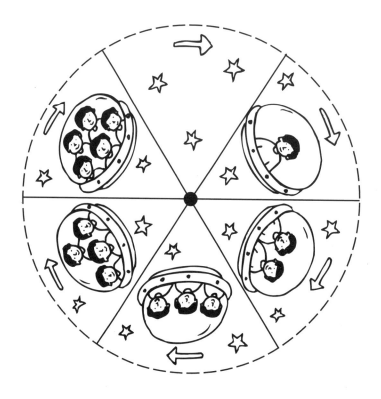

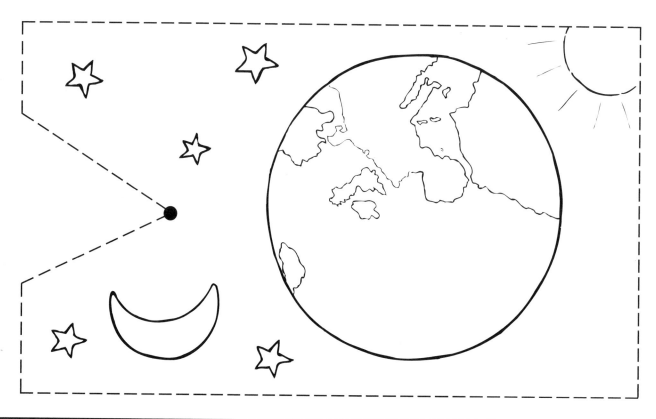

Picture cards

Colour in and cut out the cards.

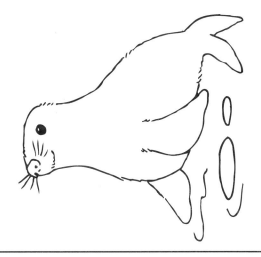

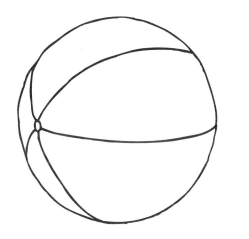

Sewing a calendar

Can you weave some thread through the trees?

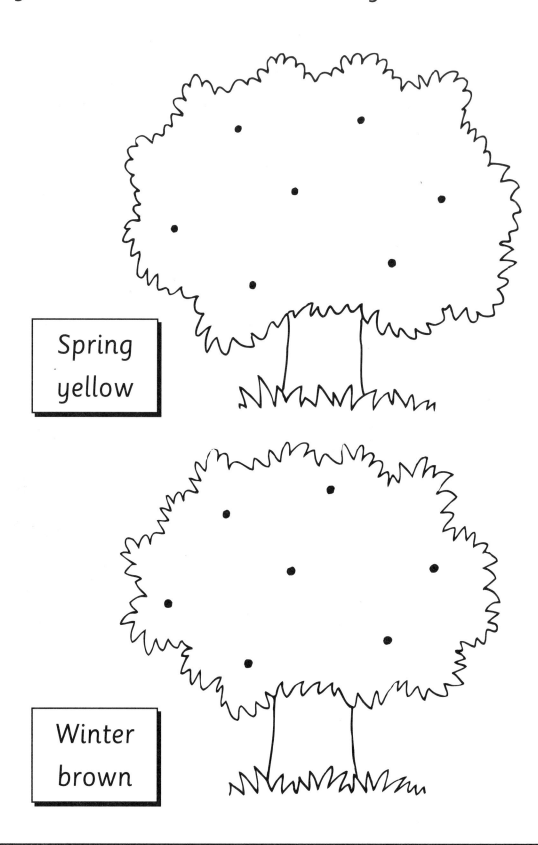

Spring
yellow

Winter
brown

Toy box dot-to-dot

Join the dots. Now fill the box with pictures of toys.

The buns and cakes game

Play a game and decorate the buns and cakes.

Learning in the Early Years - Photocopiable Activities
Physical Development

A sailor went to sea

Use a pencil to follow these waves.

Incy Wincy Spider

Colour in and cut out the pictures.

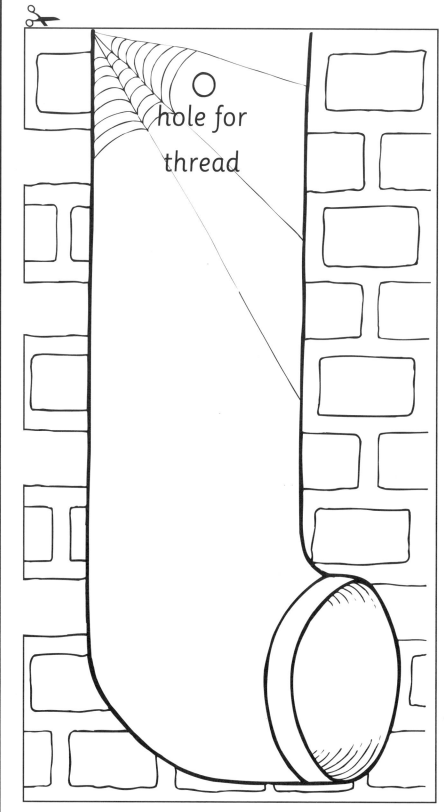

hole for thread

tape thread to spider

Hands and feet

Make a spinner.

one foot

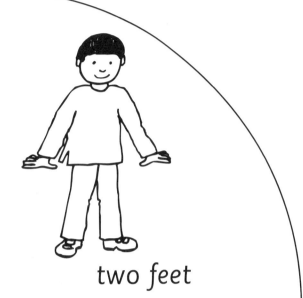

two feet

one hand, two feet

two hands, two feet

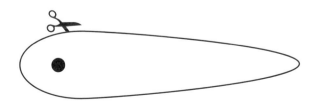

spinner

Humpty's fall

Colour or paint Humpty and cut him out.

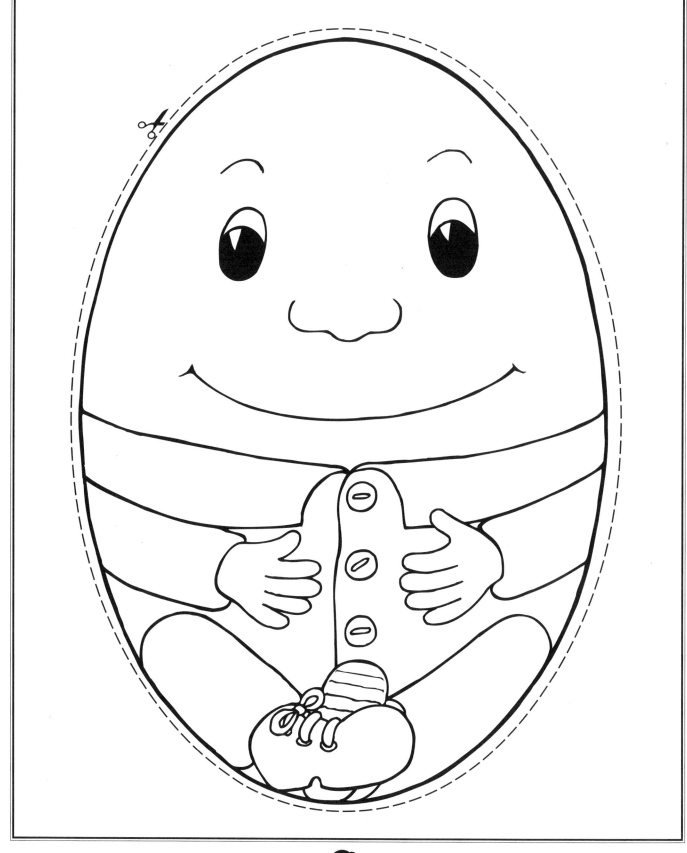

Ball rolling

Colour in and cut out.

A patterned fish

Finish these patterns and bubbles with bright colours.

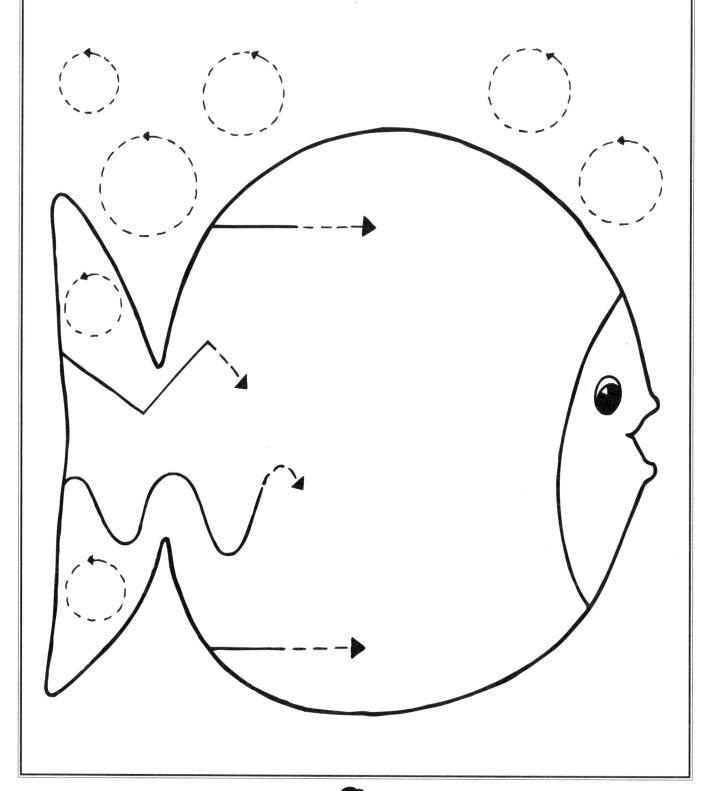

chapter three

Balance and awareness of space

Achieving balance and spatial awareness are very important aspects of every child's physical development. The skills will help them in practical activities such as dance, apparatus work and physical play, as well as during constructive play, drawing, reading and writing.

PAGE 39–42

Animal masks

Learning objective
To construct a simple mask and use it to inspire movement and mime.

What to do
Invite each child to select an animal mask to decorate from the available choices: a mouse, a cat, a rabbit or a bird. Help them to cut around the dotted lines of their chosen mask, and to cut out the eye holes. Encourage a high degree of independence as the children decorate their masks using collage materials or paints. Help them to add wool or ribbon ties.

Invite the children to wear their animal masks while they mime the movements of the relevant animal in a room with plenty of space. If possible, play a recording of some instrumental music for the children to move to. Include tunes which have fast and slow sections to inspire them to use a range of fast and slow actions.

PAGE 43–44

'I can...' booklet

Learning objective
To complete an action booklet, developing gross motor skills.

What to do
This is an activity for individuals, pairs or small groups. Photocopy the two 'I can...' pages and secure them together to form a four page booklet for each child. Help the children to write their name after the words 'I am...' and invite them to colour in the action pictures. Read the booklet with the children and encourage them to do the actions (hopping, skipping, jumping and rolling).

Insert blank pages to include other actions in the booklet. Challenge the children further by inviting them to select two or three of the actions to create a short sequence of movement, for example jump and roll or hop, skip and jump. Let the children take their booklets home to practise the actions with their parents.

Body shape spinner game

PAGE 45

Learning objective
To explore body shapes; to develop gross motor skills and spatial awareness.

What to do
Make one enlarged photocopy of the spinner and secure it onto thin card. Cut out the picture circle and spinner arm. Attach the spinner arm using a paper fastener.

Use the spinner with a small or large group of children. Display the 'Body shape spinner' circle in a room with music facilities and with enough space for the children to move around safely. Invite the children to dance, hop, skip and so on to the music. When the music stops, ask each child to make one of the four body shapes shown on the circle. Now spin the spinner arm, all the children making the shape shown are 'out'. Play continues with the rest of the children until a winner is found. Alternatively, play for fun, with everyone joining in again after each spin.

Robot skittles

PAGE 46

Learning objective
To develop throwing and aiming skills and spatial awareness.

What to do

Make two copies of the sheet in three different sizes if possible: A3, A4 and A5, to produce six robot pictures: two small, two medium and two large. Invite the children to colour in and cut out the pictures. Tape or glue the robot pictures onto six plastic bottles of appropriate size.

Place the robot skittles on the floor and invite the children to take it in turns to roll a ball, or to throw a beanbag at them. Challenge them further by increasing the space between the children and the skittles.

Alternatively, extend the activity by including number scores on to each robot. Help the children to add up their scores as they knock the robots over.

PAGE 47

The Yellow Chalk Road

Learning objective

To experience different ways of moving and balancing the body

What to do:

A game for small or large groups. Introduce the children to the story of *The Wizard of Oz* by Frank L Baum (Penguin). Enlarge the sheet to A3, and cut out the three pictures of Dorothy, the Scarecrow and the Tin Man. Invite the children to colour them in. Stick each picture onto a sheet of folded card, so that it is free-standing.

Use yellow chalk to mark out a long line around the playground for the children to follow, include sections which are straight, wavy, zigzagged, curving and so on. Position the three pictures around the course. Invite the children to move around the course. When they pass the picture of the Tin Man they should move 'stiffly', when they reach the picture of the Scarecrow, their movements should change to 'floppy', and when they pass the picture of Dorothy they should 'skip'.

PAGE 48-49

Where's that dragon?

Learning objective

To develop spatial awareness and ability to play fairly.

What to do:

This is a game for small or large groups. Make enlarged copies of both 'Where's that dragon?' sheets. Invite the children

to colour or paint them so they are bright and eye-catching. Cut the pictures on the 'Part 1' sheet into four and position each one in the four corners of your room, making sure there is enough space for the children to move around freely and safely. Cut out the four pictures on the 'Part 2' sheet and mount them onto four separate sheets of card. Place them in a pile face down.

Encourage the children to move around the room in a specified way (such as tiptoes) in the same direction. After a short while, make a noise to represent a dragon's footsteps (such as a few loud claps or bangs on a tambour). The children should immediately choose one picture to sit by, as a place to 'hide' from the 'dragon'. When all the children are seated, turn over the top card to show 'where the dragon is'. All the children who are 'hiding' in the same place have been caught by the dragon. These children should sit out for the next round. Shuffle the cards and repeat the game.

Make-believe minibeasts

PAGE 50

Learning objective

To construct 'antennae' head-wear and use them to inspire large body movements.

What to do

This construction activity for individual children leads on to a movement activity for groups of children.

You will need an area, inside or out, with enough space for the children to move freely and safely. If possible go on a minibeast hunt outdoors or look at pictures of animals with antennae. Invite each child to decorate some antennae using pens, paints, glitter or collage materials, for a make-believe minibeast. Help them to cut around the dotted lines and to glue their antennae onto a strip of card. Bend and secure the card to fit around the child's head.

Invite them to wear their antennae while they make up a range of strange and exaggerated body movements to emulate a make-believe minibeast. You could provide suggestions such as 'Can you fly, crawl, swim, jump, wriggle?' Ask the children to change speed, direction, body shape, body height while avoiding bumping into each other!

Rabbit mask

Colour in and cut out your mask.

Mouse mask

Colour in and cut out your mask.

Learning in the Early Years - Photocopiable Activities
Physical Development

Cat mask

Colour in and cut out your mask.

Bird mask

Colour in and cut out your mask.

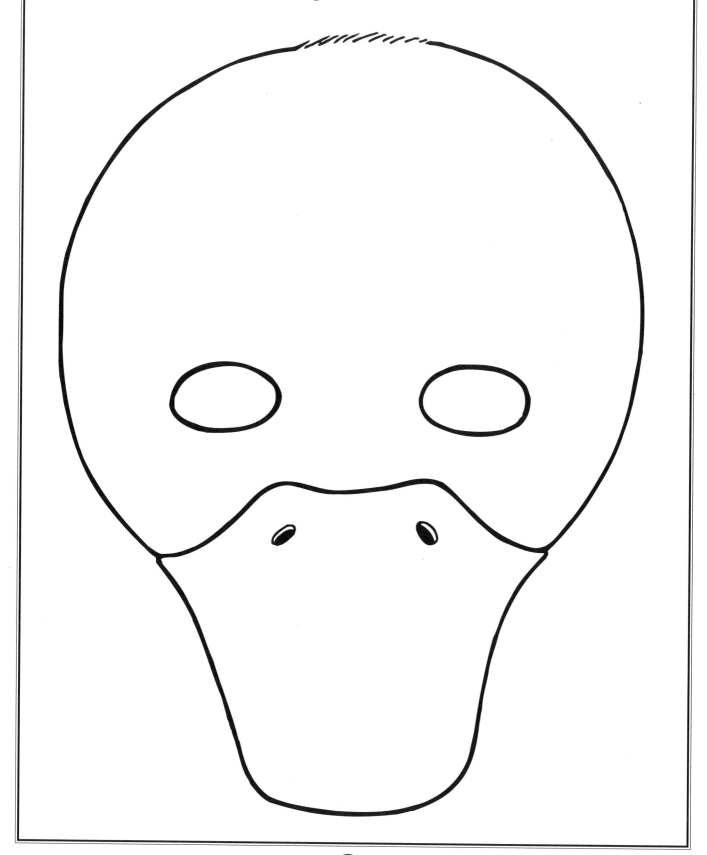

'I can...' booklet

Make these pictures into a book.

I am _____

I can hop

I am _____

I can jump

'I can...' booklet

Make these pictures into a book.

I am _____

I can roll

I am _____

I can skip

Body shape spinner game

Make a spinner.

tall shapes

wide shapes

flat

curled

spinner arm

Robot skittles

Colour in and cut out these robots.

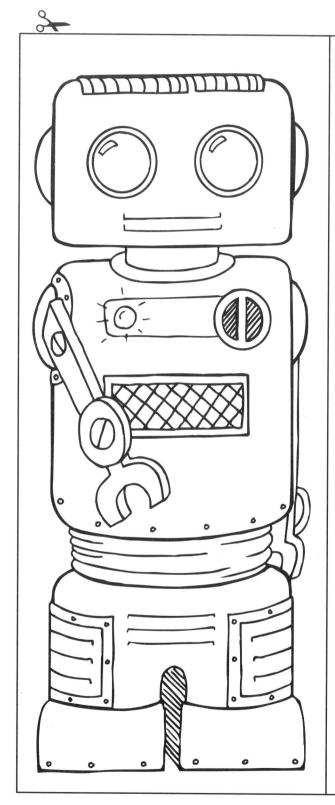
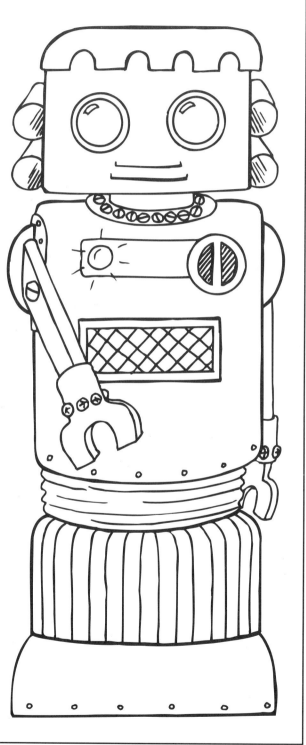

The Yellow Chalk Road

Colour in and cut out.

The Tin Man

The Scarecrow

Dorothy

Where's that dragon? Part 1

Colour in and cut into four picture cards.

Where's that dragon? Part 2

Colour in and cut into four picture cards.

Make-believe minibeasts

Colour in and cut out these make-believe antennae.

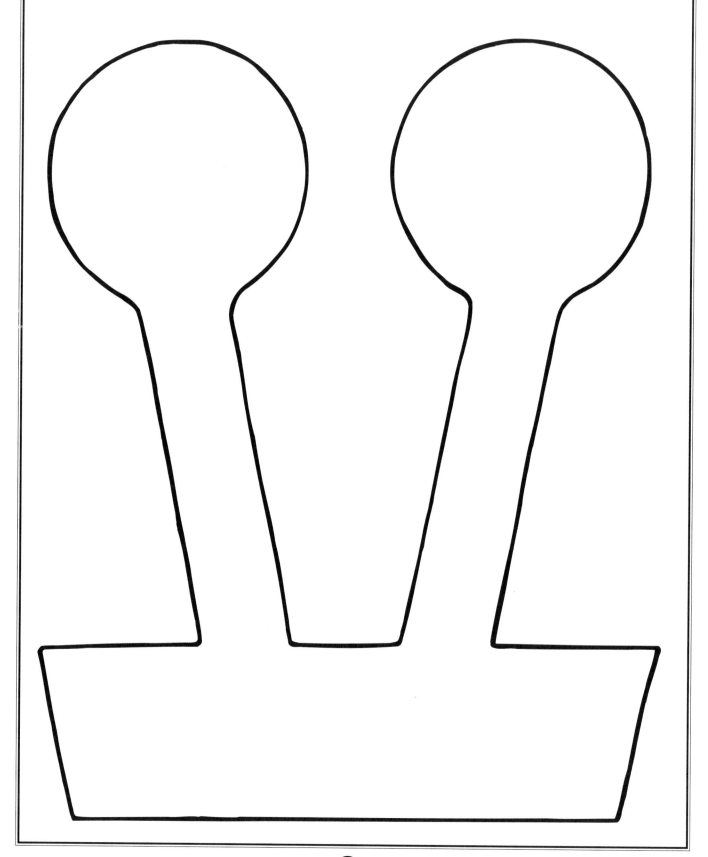

Learning in the Early Years - Photocopiable Activities
Physical Development

chapter four

Using malleable materials

This chapter aims to provide an interesting and varied range of activities based on using malleable materials such as clay, Plasticine, sand and dough. It offers ideas to stimulate the children's senses, especially the sense of touch, with practical approaches.

PAGE 54

Number patterns

Learning objective
To gain experience of rolling and manipulating a malleable material to create numbers.

What to do
This activity can be used with individuals or small groups. Enlarge the photocopiable sheet to A3 and cut out the individual numbers. If possible, laminate each section. Provide each child with a fist-sized lump of clay or firm dough and show them how to roll it into long sausage shapes. Help them to use the individual numbers as templates, on which they lay their clay (or dough) to form a three-dimensional copy. When they have finished, leave the clay (or dough) numbers to dry.

Encourage each child to paint and varnish their number or numbers. Invite the children to turn their numbers into keepsakes or paperweights by securing felt (or another non-fraying fabric) to the back of each number using strong adhesive. Alternatively, create some number wall plaques by attaching a small loop of thread to the back of each number.

House mosaic

PAGE 55

Learning objective
To develop fine motor skills.

What to do
Make copies of the house picture to provide sufficient for the children to have one each. If possible laminate the sheets or cover them in plastic film.

Show the children some pictures of mosaics to let them understand the idea. Provide them with softened Plasticine in a variety of colours and encourage them to apply small pieces of Plasticine over the house picture until the picture is completely covered, like a mosaic.

As a follow-up, invite the children to make up their own 'mosaic' pictures and patterns.

PAGE 56

Mud pie flowers
Learning objective
To experience handling different consistencies of a malleable mixture.
What to do
This activity can be undertaken by pairs of children or individuals. Provide each child with a copy of the sheet. Invite them to colour the flowers in and then to cut them out around the dotted lines. Help them to attach a stick (garden cane or an old pencil) to each flower. Place the flowers to one side. Next, provide aprons, a tray of mud, some water, plastic flowerpots and small garden tools. Let them use the items to experiment in finding a mixture which is thick enough to hold their paper flowers securely.

PAGE 57

Shiny decorations
Learning objective
To use materials carefully; to develop manual dexterity.
What to do
Provide each child with an A4 copy of the sheet. Encourage them to spread adhesive over one shape on the sheet at a time, and to carefully sprinkle glitter on top. When dry, help them to tip the excess glitter into a container for re-use. When all the decorations are finished, encourage the children to cut around the shapes and mount them onto folded card to create special gift tags. Alternatively, let them put glitter on the reverse side of each shape too and then hang them as mobiles.

PAGE 58

Floppy frog pattern
Learning objective
To experience making a malleable toy; to develop fine motor skills.
What to do:
Provide each child with an A4 or A3 copy of the sheet. Help them to cut around the thick black line to create a paper pattern, and to pin the pattern onto non-fraying fabric, such as felt. Adult help may be required to assist the children in each cutting out two fabric frog shapes. Help the children to glue or sew around the edge of the shapes, leaving a small gap for stuffing. Supervise the children as they carefully place a small amount of pasta or lentils into the gap. (Make sure the children do not attempt to eat the pasta or lentils.) Help the children to sew or glue the gap together and to cut out and glue felt eyes to add to their floppy frogs.

PAGE 59

Teddy bears picnic
Learning objective
To develop manual dexterity.
What to do:
Use as an A4 activity for individuals, or enlarge the sheet to A3 for paired work. Provide each child (or pair of children) with a copy of the sheet and ask them to colour it in. Invite them to use play dough or Plasticine to model mini cups, plates and food. Place the items on the picnic sheet to create a three-dimensional picnic scene and use the scenes for imaginative play using small teddies or play figures.

PAGE 60

A seaside scene
Learning objective
To explore texture through the use of malleable materials.
What to do
Use as an A4 activity for individual children, or enlarge to A3 for paired work. Provide each child (or pair) with a copy of the sheet. Make up a thick flour and water paste for them to create a textured 'rough sea'. When the sheets are dry, invite the children to colour or collage the ship and to sprinkle sand over adhesive for the seabed. Mount the pictures onto card and display at the children's own height for them to see and touch. Alternatively, hang a calendar or notepad from the picture for the children to take home.

PAGE 61

Making dough
Learning objective
To experience handling different consistencies of a malleable mixture.
What to do
This is an activity for individuals or pairs of children. Provide the children with all appropriate tools and ingredients detailed on the sheet. Make sure the children and the area in which you are working are protected from spills and splashes.

Read the rebus 'making dough' sheet

with the children. Maintain constant supervision as the children follow the instructions, although allow them a high degree of independence as they spoon, pour and mix the ingredients. Encourage them to experiment making mixtures which are 'sloppy', 'stiff', 'gooey', 'crumbly' and 'just right' for making things. Invite the children to take this sheet home to use with their parents.

PAGE 62

Sandcastle flags
Learning objective
To develop fine and gross motor skills while constructing flags and creating large sand sculptures.
What to do
This can be used as an activity for individuals, or groups of up to four children. Encourage the children to colour in and cut out the four flags. Provide four lolly sticks or dowelling rods to use as flag sticks and help the children to tape their flags to the flag sticks.

Encourage the children to build large castles or other sculptures from damp sand in the sand tray and place the flags in their castles.

PAGE 63

The caterpillar game
Learning objective
To use Plasticine to develop manipulative skills.
What to do
This is a game for two to three players. Provide one game sheet and a dice (showing dots, figures or words 1–6) for the group and different coloured Plasticine for each player.

The players take turns to throw the dice and to place a ball of Plasticine over the matching section on the caterpillar. If the matching section is already covered, the dice is passed on. Play continues until the caterpillar is completely covered. The winner is the player with the most sections in their colour.

PAGE 64

A 3D fish pond
Learning objective
To gain experience of manipulating a malleable material; to create a three-dimensional scene.
What to do
This is an activity for individuals or pairs of children. Provide each child, or pair of children with the sheet. Invite the children to colour the pond blue and the lily pads green. Provide each child with a large lump of brown or grey Plasticine (or play dough). Show them how to break off sections of the Plasticine and roll into uneven shapes to represent stones or rocks. Encourage the children to surround their pond with these stones or rocks by placing them on the speckled areas of the sheet.

When complete, provide orange Plasticine (or play dough) for the children to make goldfish. Alternatively, provide coloured or shiny paper for the children to cut into fish shapes. Invite the children to press pieces of real grass around the edges of the 'stones' or 'rocks' to complete the three-dimensional scene.

Number patterns

Cut out the numbers. Use clay or dough to make a model number.

House mosaic

Can you make a Plasticine picture?

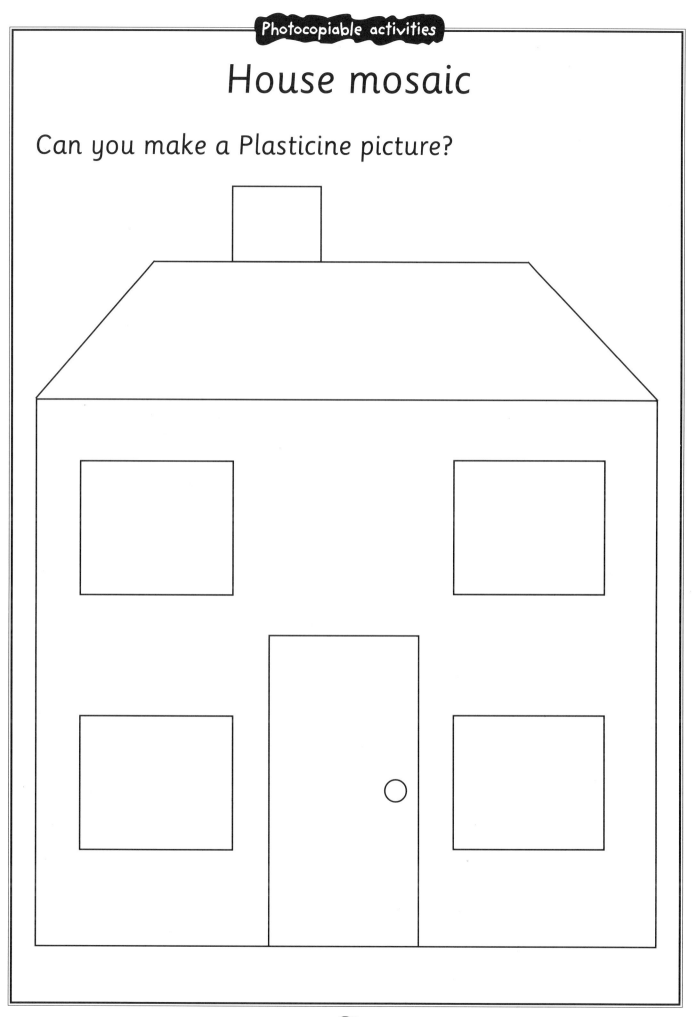

Mud pie flowers

Colour in and cut out these flowers.

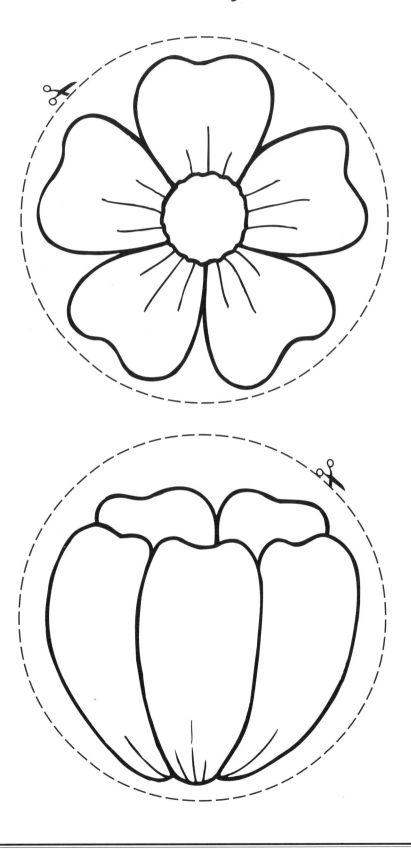

Shiny decorations

Stick glitter on these shapes.

Floppy frog pattern

Cut out this shape to make a frog.

Learning in the Early Years - Photocopiable Activities
Physical Development

Teddy bears picnic

Make cups and food to make a picnic scene.

A seaside scene

Make a textured picture.

Making dough

Use these ingredients to make different mixtures.
You need

food
colouring

plain
flour

salt

water

bowl

tablespoon

What to do

Use a to place  and

into a  . Add a little . Add ,

one drop at a time.

Find a mixture which is floppy or stiff, gooey or crumbly.

Now find a mix which is just right for making things.

Sandcastle flags

Colour in and cut out these flags.

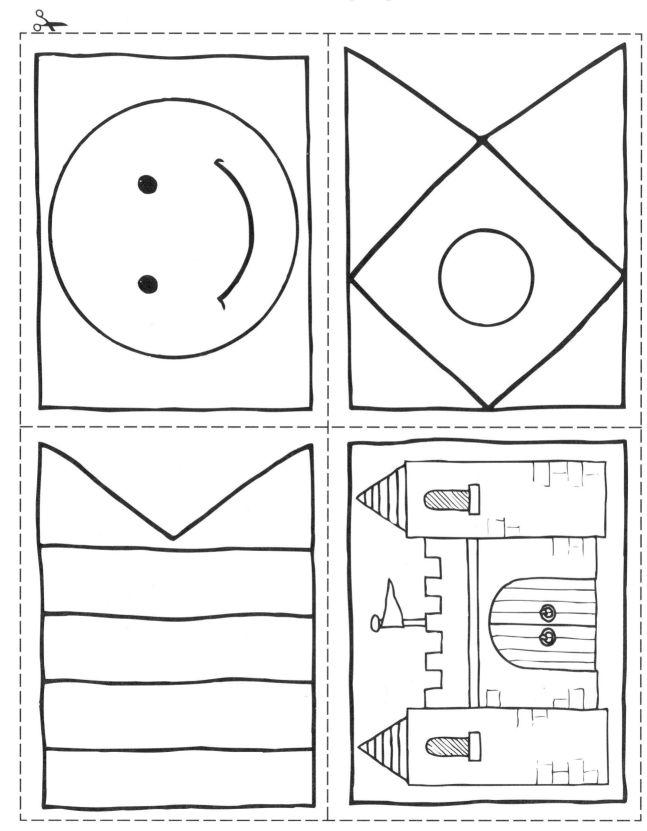

Learning in the Early Years - Photocopiable Activities
Physical Development

The caterpillar game

Throw a dice and cover the caterpillar.

A 3D fish pond

Use coloured pens, paints, Plasticine or dough to make a pond.

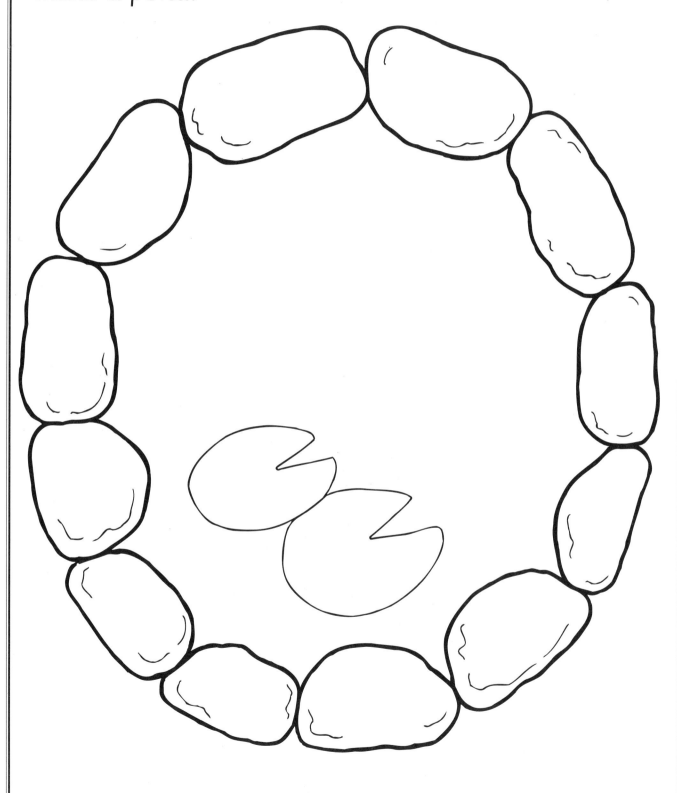